Waltzy About That

Chris Gumbley
(born 1958)

senza Ped.

4

Rondeau

from *Abdelazar*

arr. James Rae

Henry Purcell
(1659-1695)

D.C. al Fine

Barcarolle

Tim Watts
(born 1979)

In the Hall of the Mountain King

from *Peer Gynt* Suite no. 1 op. 46

arr. David Adlam

Edvard Grieg
(1843-1907)

Tritsch-Tratsch Polka

op. 214

arr. David Adlam

Johann Strauss II
(1825-1899)

Tritsch-Tratsch = Chit-Chat

The Deep Blue Yonder

Robert Ramskill
(born 1950)

Rondo alla Turca

no. 3 from *Corbeille de roses* op. 68

arr. Andrew Challinger

Johann Friedrich Burgmüller
(1806-1874)

Rondo alla Turca = Turkish Rondo

Près de berceau

op. 58 no. 3

arr. Patrick Gundry-White

Moritz Moszkowski
(1854–1925)

Près de berceau = Near the cradle

Bunch of Fives

Chris Gumbley
(born 1958)

Andante grazioso

3rd movement from Trio for Clarinet, Cello and Piano op. 114

arr. David Adlam

Johannes Brahms
(1833–1897)

36

Soldier, Soldier

Jim Parker
(born 1934)

Orientale

no. 9 from *Kaleidoscope* op. 50

arr. Robin Hagues

César Cui
(1835-1918)